A Big Laugh

Written by Jill Eggleton

Illustrated by Raymond McGrath

Dad put the sausages
on the barbecue.
"I will make lunch,"
he said.

Dad went to water
the garden.

The kids looked
out the window.
They saw smoke.
They saw
black sausages!

"Dad! Dad!"
shouted the kids.

"Help!" said Dad.
He put the hose
on the barbecue.

"**Yuck**!" said the kids.
"The sausages are black
and the sausages are wet!"

Dad went inside.
"We are hungry,"
said the kids.

"I will make sandwiches,"
said Dad.
"We have some bread."

The kids looked
at the bread.
"**Yuck!**" said the kids.
"We can't have this bread."

Dad looked at the bread.
"**Oops!**" he said.
"Ants!"

Dad got
the vacuum cleaner.
Whoosh!
The ants went up
the vacuum cleaner.

But . . .
whooooooooosh!
The bread went up
the vacuum cleaner, too!

Dad and the kids
laughed and laughed
and . . . **laughed!**

A Comic Strip

Guide Notes

Title: A Big Laugh

Stage: Early (2) - Yellow

Genre: Fiction

Approach: Guided Reading

Processes: Thinking Critically, Exploring Language, Processing Information

Written and Visual Focus: Comic Strip

Word Count: 135

THINKING CRITICALLY

(sample questions)
- What do you think this story could be about?
- Focus on the title and discuss.
- Why do you think the sausages got burned?
- Why do you think Dad was watering the garden?
- How else do you think Dad could have got the ants off the bread?
- What do you think the kids might have for lunch now?

EXPLORING LANGUAGE

Terminology
Title, cover, illustrations, author, illustrator

Vocabulary
Interest words: barbecue, yuck, whooosh, laughed, ants, oops
High-frequency words: inside, make
Positional words: on, out, inside, up

Print Conventions
Capital letter for sentence beginnings and names (**D**ad), full stops, commas, quotation marks, exclamation marks